Developing Lit
WORD LEVEL

WORD-LEVEL ACTIVITIES FOR THE LITERACY HOUR

year

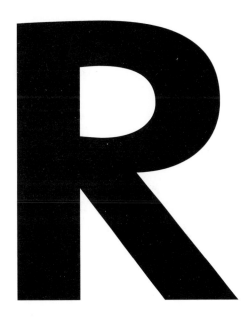

Ray Barker

Christine Moorcroft

A & C BLACK

Reprinted 1999 (twice), 2000
First published in 1998 by
A&C Black (Publishers) Limited
35 Bedford Row, London WC1R 4JH

ISBN O-7136-4989-5

The authors and publisher would like to thank the
following teachers for their advice in producing this
series of books: Tracy Adam; Ann Hart; Lydia Hunt; Hazel Jacob;
Madeleine Madden; Helen Mason; Yvonne Newman; Annette Norman;
Katrin Trigg; Judith Wells.

A CIP catalogue record for this book is
available from the British Library.

Printed in Great Britain by
St Edmundsbury Press Ltd, Bury St Edmunds, Suffolk.

Contents

Introduction

Developing Literacy: Word Level supports the teaching of reading and writing by providing a series of activities to develop essential skills in reading and spelling: word recognition and phonics. The activities are designed to be carried out in the time allocated to independent work during the Literacy Hour and therefore should be relatively 'teacher-free'. The focus is on children investigating words and spelling patterns, generating their own words in accordance with what they have learned and, if possible, recognising and devising rules and strategies to enable them to become independent in their recording and further investigation of language.

The activities presented in **Developing Literacy: Word Level** support the learning objectives of the National Literacy Strategy at word level. Each book
- includes activities which focus on phonics, spelling, word recognition and vocabulary;
- develops children's understanding of sound-spelling relationships;
- helps children to extend their vocabulary by challenging them to talk about and investigate the meanings of words which they find difficult;
- promotes independent work during the Literacy Hour;
- has extension activities on each page which reinforce and develop what the children have learned;
- includes brief notes for teachers at the bottom of most pages.

Some of the activities focus on the high frequency words listed in the National Literacy Strategy's *Framework for Teaching*. These are lists of words to be learned to be recognised on sight. At Key Stage 1, they are words which the children need to know in order to tackle even very simple texts. Some are regular but others, such as 'said' and 'water' do not follow regular phonic spelling patterns. At Key Stage 2, an additional list of medium frequency words is added which children often find difficulty in spelling.

The activities are presented in a way which requires the children to read the words rather than just guessing the answers or 'filling in the spaces'. Sometimes they are asked to turn over the sheet and then write a list of words; a partner could read the words aloud for them to write. Working with partners or in groups is encouraged so that the children can check one another's reading and co-operate to complete the activities or to play games. It is also useful for the children to show their work to the rest of the class and to explain their answers in order to reinforce and develop their own learning and that of others in the class.

Children need to 'Look, Say, Cover, Write and Check' (LSCWCh) words on a regular basis in order to learn their spellings. This has mostly been left to the teacher to initiate. However, it is used on some pages and is presented as follows:

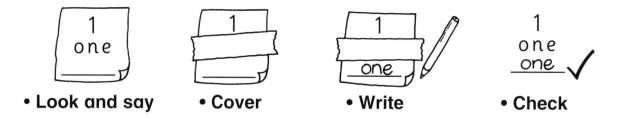

- **Look and say**   • **Cover**   • **Write**   • **Check**

Extension

Each activity sheet ends with a challenge (**Now try this!**) which reinforces and extends the children's learning and provides the teacher with an opportunity for assessment. Where children are asked to carry out an activity, the instructions are clear to enable them to work independently. The teacher may decide to amend this before photocopying, depending on his or her knowledge of the children's abilities and speed of working, for example by reducing the number of words that the child is asked to write.

 • **Write four other words which start with** t h **.**

Organisation

For many of the activities it will be useful to have a range of dictionaries, fiction and non-fiction books, coloured pencils, scissors and squared paper available and easily accessible. Several activities can be re-used to provide more practice in different letters or sounds, by masking the words and/or letters and replacing them with others of the teacher's choice, such as on page 15.

To help teachers to select appropriate learning experiences for their pupils, the activities are grouped into sections within each book. The pages are **not** intended to be presented in the order in which they appear in the books. The teacher should select the appropriate pages to support the work in progress. For more able children the teacher may want to adapt the activity sheets by masking the words and letters and replacing them with more demanding examples.

Many activities will be completed entirely on the activity sheets. On others, particularly in the extension activities, the children will need to work on the back of the page, on a separate sheet of paper or in an exercise book. Such activities include

- Draw ...
- Write ...

or
- Cut out and collect ...

It is useful for children to keep their own **word banks** with the new words they have learned. These could be general or for a specific theme on which the class is working, such as animals. Children should be encouraged to make a note of any words they cannot read so that they can add them to the word bank. The class could also have a **word wall** display to which they can add new words.

Structure of the Literacy Hour

The recommended structure of the Literacy Hour for Key Stage 1 is as follows:

Whole class introduction	15 min	Shared text work (balance of reading and writing) in which the teacher reads or writes a piece of text with the class, to elicit the children's participation in discussion of the topic to be taught.
Whole class activity	15 min	Focused word work in which the children contribute to a teacher-led activity arising from the whole class introduction.
Group work Independent work (rest of class)	20 min	The teacher works with groups of children on guided text work. The other children could work independently, for example, from an activity in one of the **Developing Literacy** series (**Word Level**, **Sentence Level** or **Text Level**).
Whole class plenary session	10 min	The teacher leads a review of what has been learned by consolidating teaching points, reviewing, reflecting and sharing the children's ideas and the results of their work in the lesson.

The following flow chart shows an example of the way in which an activity from this book can be used to achieve the required organisation of the Literacy Hour.

Alphabet necklaces (page 14)

Whole class introduction	**15 min**
Cheer the alphabet ('Give me an 'a'; give me a 'b', and so on). The children can take turns to be the 'cheer-leader'.	

Whole class activity	**15 min**
Provide an alphabet frieze on which some of the letters have been covered using sticky notes. Ask the children to name the hidden letters.	

Group work 20 min	**Independent work** 20 min
Work with one group of children who thread on to string or coloured laces large beads with (lower-case) letters written on them.	The others work independently from **Alphabet necklaces** (page 14) from **Developing Literacy: Word Level Year R**.

Whole class plenary session	**10 min**
The children write lower-case letters of the alphabet on to circles, which they arrange along a painted 'string' on a wall display to make a complete 'alphabet necklace'.	

Teachers' notes

Very brief notes are provided at the end of most pages. They give ideas and suggestions for maximising the effectiveness of the activity sheets. They may make suggestions for the whole class introduction, the plenary session or, possibly, for follow-up work using an adapted version of the activity sheet. Before photocopying, these notes could be masked.

Using the activity sheets

Brief information is given here about the work within each section of **Developing Literacy: Word Level Year R**. Suggestions are also given for additional activities.

Alphabetical order

This section helps the children to recognise the letters of the alphabet, to learn their names and to put them in the correct order.

Letter snakes (pages 9-12) are concerned mainly with letter recognition (lower-case), but they also provide handwriting practice.

Ask the children to find the letters which are made from two snakes: why is 'f' made from two snakes? They could write each letter and notice that they do not lift their pencils off the paper when they write 'a', 'b', 'c', 'd' and 'e', but that when they write 'f' they do. Can they think of other letters with which they do this?

Alphabet dot-to-dot (page 13), **Alphabet necklaces** (page 14), **Alphabet flags** (page 15) and **Alphabet snakes** (page 16) reinforce the learning of the alphabet by asking the children to complete letter sequences. During the introductory session, give 26 children each a card on which a (lower-case) letter has been written or printed. Invite those who have 'a' to 'e' to come to the front of the class and arrange themselves in alphabetical order, then 'f' to 'j', and so on, until the whole alphabet is represented. Any children who do not have a letter should check that the order is correct, and then say the letter names in order.

Names

This section reinforces the children's knowledge of upper- and lower-case letters and their names, while also providing practice in the sounds made by each letter. The children are provided with more practice in writing their own names and those of their friends.

In **Ben's bag** (pages 17-18) and **Zena's zoo** (page 19), names are used to help the children to match and discriminate between upper-case letters and their lower-case counterparts. They practise writing their own names and those of their friends. They consolidate their knowledge of the names of letters and develop phonic knowledge through using the sounds of the letters. These games can first be played orally with a small group of children or even with the whole class. With the children, read the words on page 17: what do they notice about each thing which is added to Ben's bag? Some of them might notice that they are in alphabetical order. If necessary, provide an alphabet strip, to help the children find which letter comes next as each item is added to the list. **Zena's zoo** can be introduced in the same way. Both of these activities introduce, at a very simple level, the idea of topic-based word banks and glossaries.

As an extension, the children can make up their own versions of the game, based on subjects in which they are interested, for example, flowers, birds, makes of cars or brands of sweets.

b and d (page 20) reinforces recognition of the letters 'b' and 'd', presenting a mnemonic with which to help the children to write these letters the right way round.

Letter partners Aa to Nn (page 21) and **Letter partners Oo to Zz** (page 22) provide practice in writing upper- and lower-case letters.

In **Letter shopping** (page 23), the children learn to recognise the beginning sounds of words while developing their knowledge of upper- and lower-case letters; they also practise writing their own names. During the plenary session, invite the children to say a person's name; write the name on a board or a large sheet of paper and ask the children to think what he or she might buy which begins with the same letter. Write the word for it. This could lead to a classroom collage of children's paintings of people with the things they buy. The display could have an 'alphabet' border consisting of upper- and lower-case letters.

People and places (page 24) provides more practice with upper- and lower-case letters, initial sounds of words and the children's own names. They could make up 'silly stories' about places to which people go which begin with the same letters as their names.

Name link (page 25) gives practice in developing recognition of initial sounds of words. It avoids giving the words for the objects depicted because the focus is on the sounds, rather than on the letters themselves.

High frequency words

This section helps the children to recognise, read and spell many of the high frequency words suggested in the National Literacy Strategy's Framework for the Reception year.

Word work 1 (page 26) and **Word work 2** (page 27) ask the children to recognise and then copy words as a strategy for learning spellings. These activities have the same format, enabling the children to work independently on the second sheet.

Word work 3 (page 28) makes use of rhyme to help the children to read the words on the tree trunk. Do they notice the different ways in which the same phoneme can be spelled?

Word work 4 (page 29) introduces 'Look and Say, Cover, Write and Check'. This procedure should be followed for all new words introduced on the activity sheets in the other books in this series.

Word work 5 (page 30) introduces another strategy to help the children's spelling: looking at the shapes of words.

Word work 6 (page 31) also makes use of this strategy. Encourage the children to draw the shapes of any words which they have difficulty in reading or spelling.

Phonemes

This introduces knowledge of grapheme/phoneme correspondences (the ways in which written letters represent the smallest units of sound in a word). It encourages the children to hear and identify the initial sounds of words and to read letters at the beginnings of words (including those which are blended to make the sounds 'sh', 'ch' and 'th').

Introduce this section by playing 'I spy', to focus the children's attention on the initial sounds of words. It is important that the children recognise each sound in speech before they write it.

ball or doll (page 34) is directed towards helping the children to distinguish between 'b' and 'd' sounds and the letters 'b' and 'd', while **mat or net** (page 35) does the same with 'm' and 'n'.

First sounds bingo cards (pages 36-37) and **First sounds letter cards** (page 38) can be used in several ways:

• To play bingo, follow the Teachers' notes on the activity page.

• To play 'matching pairs': glue pages 36 and 37 on to card and cut out the individual pictures on the bingo cards. The letter cards are not needed. Turn the cards face-down. The children take turns to turn over two cards. If the two pictures begin with the same letter, they keep them. The winner is the one with the most cards when all have been turned over.

• To play 'letter-sound matching': glue pages 36-38 on to card and cut out the pictures and letters. Glue the appropriate letters on to the backs of the pictures. The children deal four cards each and leave any remaining in a pile face-down. The child to the left of the dealer begins by holding the four cards, so that the child on his or her left can see the letters only, and saying 'Which is the monkey?' (or the dog, or the frog by choosing one of the pictures he or she can see). The other child has to use the initial letter sounds to make the choice. If this is right he or she wins the card and keeps it. The child who has lost a card picks up another. The winner is the one with the most cards in his or her pile when all the cards have been played.

In **First sounds b, m, c** (page 39) and **First sounds h, p, s** (page 40), the children write the letters which represent the first sounds of different words. It is important that the children say the words first so that they learn to associate the letters with their sounds, and to write them.

Starting with sh (page 41) helps the children to learn how to recognise the letters which represent the sound 'sh'. In the extension activity the children might draw sugar. Show them how to spell 'sugar' and explain that it is different from most words which begin with the sound 'sh'.

Making words with sh (page 42) reinforces the children's recognition of the sound 'sh' and also teaches them to write it.

Starting with ch (page 43) and **Making words with ch** (page 44) encourage similar learning about the sound 'ch', and **Starting with th** (page 45) and **Making words with th** (page 46) do the same with 'th'. Independent work on the last four of these is encouraged by presenting the children with activities which have the same layouts and instructions.

End sounds (page 47) encourages the children to say the words and listen to their final phonemes, while **Word trees** (page 48), **Endings m and n** (page 49) and **Endings p and y** (page 50) also ask them to write the letters which represent those phonemes. The activities could be introduced by saying a series of words to the children and asking them to listen for a given ending. They could play 'I spy' with word ending sounds instead of with the more common version which uses the names of the initial letters of the words.

Rhyme

This develops the children's ability to understand and make up rhymes, by providing activities which encourage them to explore and work with rhyming patterns. The activities could be introduced by the use of the nursery rhymes. Another way to introduce them is to give the children clues for rhyming words, for example, 'an animal which rhymes with box' (fox), and 'something made from glass which rhymes with car' (jar).

In **Find the rhyme** (page 51), the children learn to recognise and suggest rhymes.

Rhyme line (page 52) consolidates this by asking them to find the thing which does not rhyme, and further consolidation is provided by **Rhyming pairs** (page 53).

Rhyme writing (page 54) prepares for the next section, by asking the children not only to recognise rhyming consonant-vowel-consonant words, but also to spell them.

Onset and rime

An onset is the first phoneme in a word and the rime is the part which follows it. This section encourages the children to recognise words which have the same rimes, and to use this recognition in their spelling.

Beginnings and endings 1 (page 55), **Beginnings and endings 2** (page 56) and **Beginnings and endings 3** (page 57) encourage the children to think of and write their own words with the same rime as those on the page (they have only to change the first letter). To introduce these activities, say two consonant-vowel-consonant (cvc) words such as 'red, bed' and ask the children to add another to the list. Once one sound has been exhausted, invite the children to begin a new one. They could also play this in pairs, and share their verbal and/or written lists with the rest of the class. If any words which sound the same but are spelled differently crop up, write them on a separate list (examples include 'head' with 'red', 'bed', and 'ton' with 'fun', 'sun').

Middle vowel sounds

This section develops the children's ability to hear, recognise and write the middle sounds of consonant-vowel-consonant words (grapheme/phoneme correspondence).

In **Odd one out** (page 58) and **Middle sounds pairs** (page 59), the children's attention is directed towards saying the words and listening to and recognising their middle sounds; the letters are therefore not provided.

Missing middles (page 60) consolidates the children's ability to listen to and recognise the dominant phonemes of words, and extend it by asking them to write these phonemes. Introduce the activities by writing a word on the board, missing out its middle letter. Invite the children to write a letter in the space and to read the word they have made. Another child could erase the middle letter, replace it with another and then read the word he or she has made.

Naughty Teddy (page 61) encourages the children to use the beginning and end of a 'cvc' word to guess what the word might be (there are alternatives for each; any 'real' word is correct). It prepares them for later work in which they recognise more complex words from their consonants only and learn the terms 'consonant' and 'vowel'.

Partners (page 62) requires the children to recognise words which have the same phonemes, regardless of the ways in which these phonemes are spelled, and so they are not asked to write the letters which represent the phonemes. (Different ways to spell the same phonemes are covered in **Developing Literacy: Word Level Years** 2 and 3).

Happy sound families 1 and 2 (pages 63-64) consolidate the children's learning about words with the same phonemes; the words for the objects depicted are provided in preparation for later work on the different spellings of the same phonemes.

Glossary of terms used

analogy Recognising a word, phoneme or pattern in known words and applying it to new, unfamiliar words.

ascender The part of a letter which projects upwards, for example in **b, d, h** and **k**.

blending Running together individual phonemes in pronunciation.

cluster A combination of consonant sounds before or after a vowel (or **y** used as a vowel); for example, s**pray**, **cry**, **rust**.

descender The part of a letter which projects downwards, for example in **g, j, p** and **y**.

onset The initial consonant or consonant cluster of a word or syllable; for example, **train**, **scrape**, **skate**.

phoneme The smallest unit of sound in a word. A phoneme can be represented by one to four letters; for example, **thin**, **thick**, **thigh**, **though**.

phonics The relationship between sounds and the written form of a language.

rhyme The use of words which have the same sound in their final syllable; for example, **fox/rocks**, **sore/door**.

rime The part of a word or syllable which contains the vowel and final consonant or consonant cluster, for example, **sheep**, **slow**, **foal**.

syllable A rhythmic segment of a word; for example, **can** (1 syllable) , **car- ton** (2 syllables) **can- op- y** (3 syllables), **tel- e- vis- ion** (4 syllables).

- **Trace the letter snakes.**

- **Start at the head.**

- **Finish at the tail.**

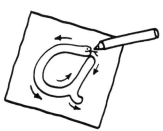

- **Say the name of the letters.**

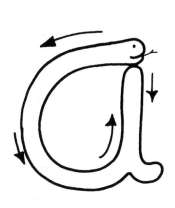
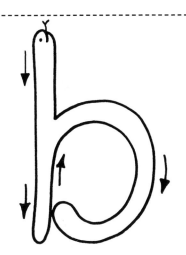

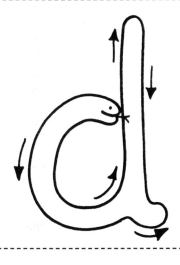

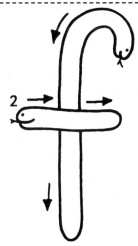

- **Cut out the letter snakes.**

- **Make an alphabet strip.**

a	b	c	d	e	f

Teachers' note For left-handed children, adjustments will need to be made to the directional arrows. Provide a strip of paper, 9-10 cm wide and 200cm long, on to which the children can glue the letters from pages 9-12, in the correct order, to make an alphabet strip. These strips can be coloured and displayed.

Developing Literacy
Word Level Year R
© A & C Black 1998

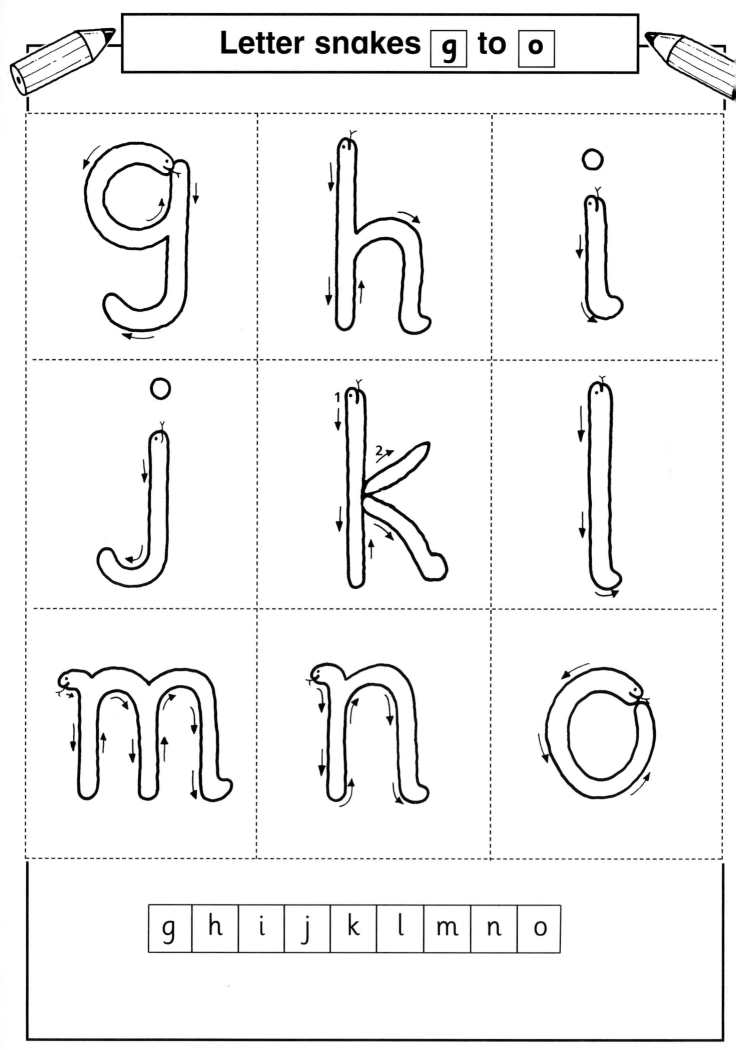

| g | h | i | j | k | l | m | n | o |

Teachers' note For left-handed children, adjustments will need to be made to the directional arrows.

Developing Literacy
Word Level Year R
© A & C Black 1998

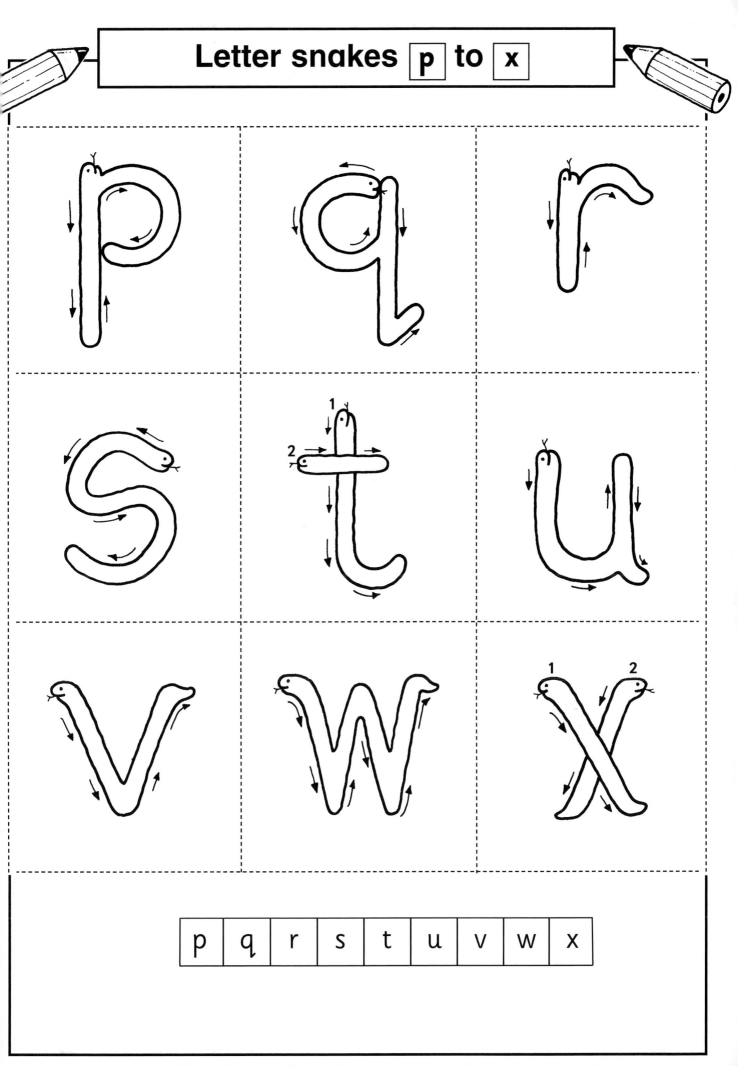

| p | q | r | s | t | u | v | w | x |

Teachers' note For left-handed children, adjustments will need to be made to the directional arrows.

Developing Literacy
Word Level Year R
© A & C Black 1998

- Trace $\boxed{y}$ and $\boxed{z}$.
- Say the names of the letters.
- Put them in your alphabet strip.

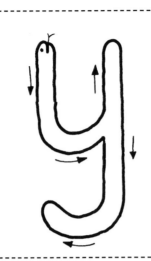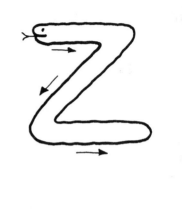

$\boxed{y \mid z}$

Now try this!

- Say the names of the letters.
- Write the letters in the boxes.

Teachers' note For left-handed children, adjustments need to be made to the arrows. **n**, **t**, **s** and **p** are not intended to be traced, but are for the children to write as normal letters. They could write all the letters of the alphabet in the same way on their alphabet strips.

Developing Literacy
Word Level Year R
© A & C Black 1998

a b c d e f g h i j k l m n o p q r s t u v w x y z

• **Join the dots in alphabetical order.**

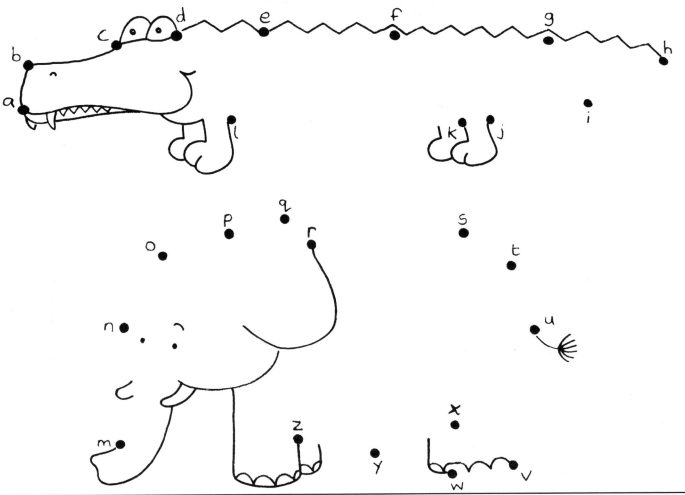

• **Write the letters by the dots.**

Join the dots.

Now try this!

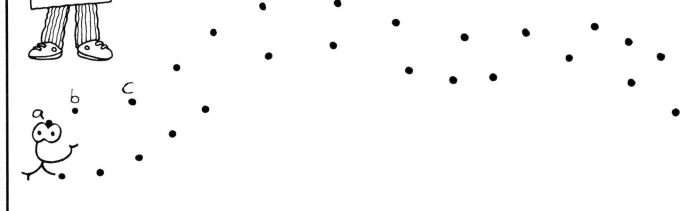

Teachers' note   The children could read aloud the names of the letters on the alphabet strip before joining the dots on the puzzle. Encourage them to say the letter names as they join the dots. Ask them to name the animals.

**Developing Literacy
Word Level Year R**
© A & C Black 1998

Alphabet necklaces

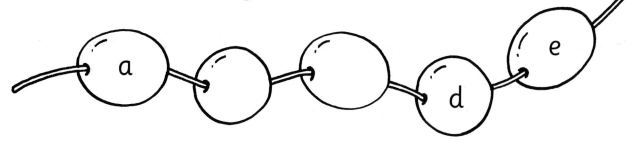

• **Write the missing letters.**

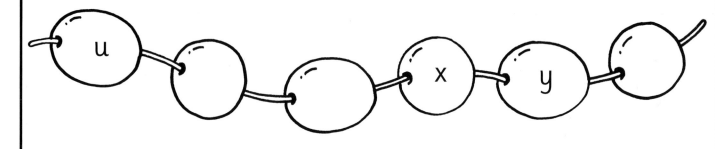

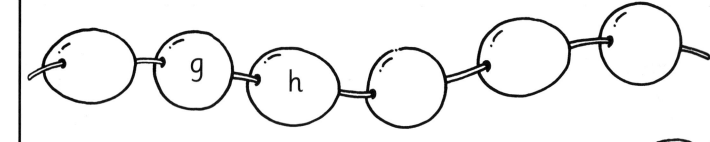

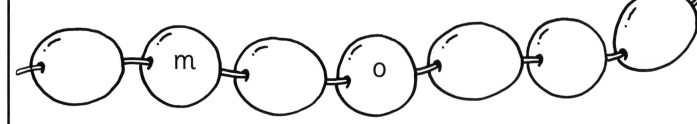

 • **Draw some alphabet necklaces for a partner to complete.**

Now try this!

Teachers' note First ask the children to read aloud the names of the letters on the alphabet strip. Write a letter and ask the children to write the ones before and after it. For some children, the alphabet strip can be masked before they complete the necklaces.

Developing Literacy
Word Level Year R
© A & C Black 1998

14

Alphabet flags

a b c d e f g h i j k l m n o p q r s t u v w x y z

• Write the letters in alphabetical order.

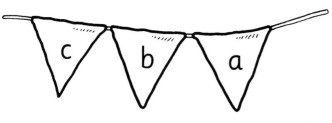

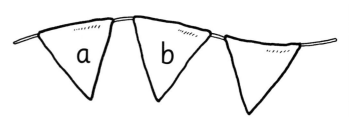

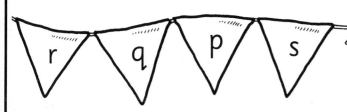

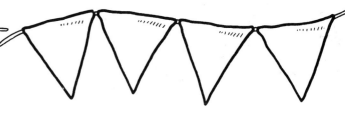

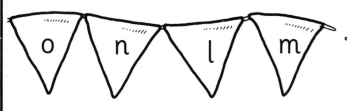

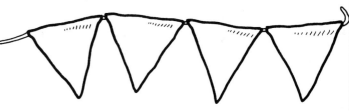

• Draw flags for these letters.

• Write them in alphabetical order.

r t u s q

Teachers' note First give the children practice in putting groups of three or four plastic letters in alphabetical order. For some children, the alphabet strip can be masked before they complete the flags.

Developing Literacy
Word Level Year R
© A & C Black 1998

15

Alphabet snakes

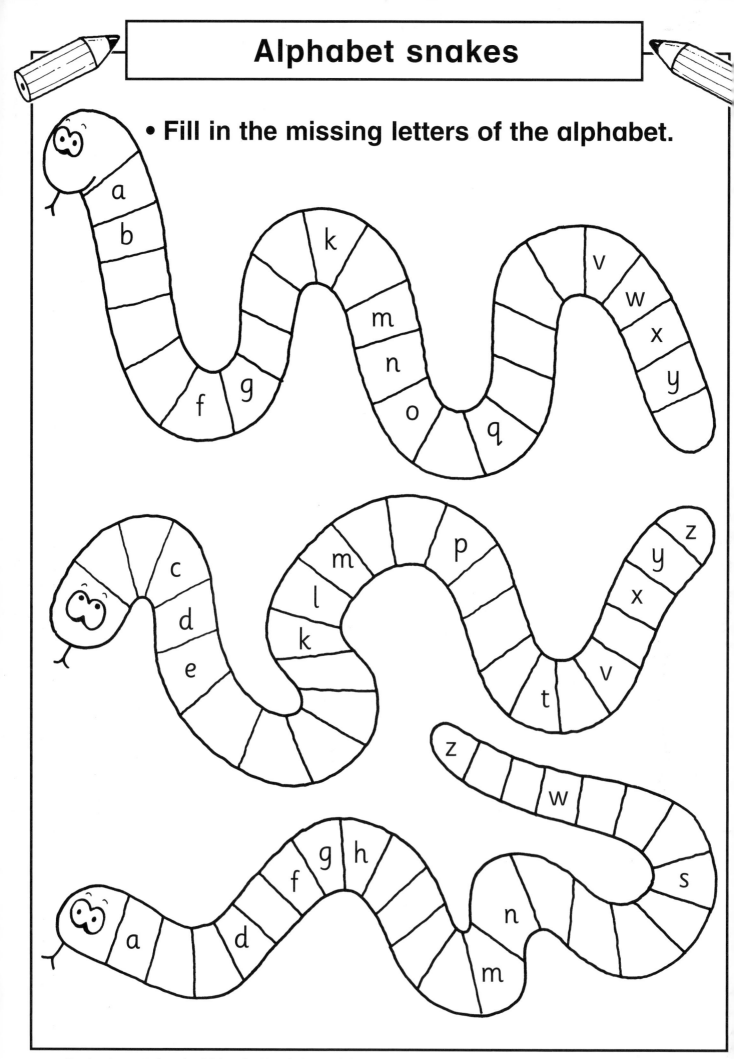

• **Fill in the missing letters of the alphabet.**

Teachers' note Before the children do this, ask them to help to arrange in alphabetical order a set of plastic or wooden letters or printed letters on cards. Remove some of the letters, mix them up and ask the children to put them in the right places.

Developing Literacy
Word Level Year R
© A & C Black 1998

Ben's bag

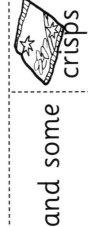

- **Say the words.**

In Ben's bag there is an  apple

| In Ben's bag there is an 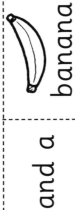 apple | and a |  banana |

In Ben's bag there is an 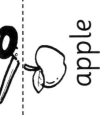 apple | a | banana | and some |  crisps

In Ben's bag there is an  apple | a | banana | some | crisps | and a |  doll

- **What comes next ?**

Use the picture cards.

Now try this!

Teachers' note   An adult should read the words with the children, pointing to the letter of the alphabet with which each item begins. The children should take turns to add, in alphabetical order, an item to Ben's bag. They will need to add the 'linking words': a, **some** and **and**. The pictures on page 18 will help them to think of new items to add to Ben's bag. Glue or photocopy page 18 on to card and cut out the pictures.

Developing Literacy
Word Level Year R
© A & C Black 1998

Ben's bag picture cards

insects

orange

umbrella

zip

helicopter

net

tie

mug

sock

yacht

grapes

letter

ruler

xylophone

fish

kettle

question

watch

egg

jam

pencil

violin

Developing Literacy

Zena's zoo picture cards

frog	lion	rabbit	zebra
elephant	koala	quail	yak
dog	jellyfish	penguin	walrus
cat	iguana	ostrich	vulture
bear	hare	newt	tiger
armadillo	gorilla	mole	snake

Teachers' note   The children can use these picture cards to play a game similar to **Ben's bag**, for example, 'In Zena's zoo there is an armadillo, a ...' and so on...
Can they spot the missing letters? They could use a picture dictionary or alphabet frieze to find the name of an animal in fairy stories which begins with **u** (unicorn).
Point out that there is one animal which begins with x, the x-ray fish.

Developing Literacy
Word Level Year R
© A & C Black 1998

- Colour **b** blue.
- Colour **d** red.

Say the words.

bed

bud

dab

- **Write three words which start with** **b** .
- **Write three words which start with** **d** .

Now try this!

Teachers' note Encourage the children to say the words and to listen to their beginning sounds. Can they think of other words which begin with **b** and end with **d** and vice versa?

Developing Literacy
Word Level Year R
© A & C Black 1998

Letter partners Aa to Nn

- **Write each letter's partner.**

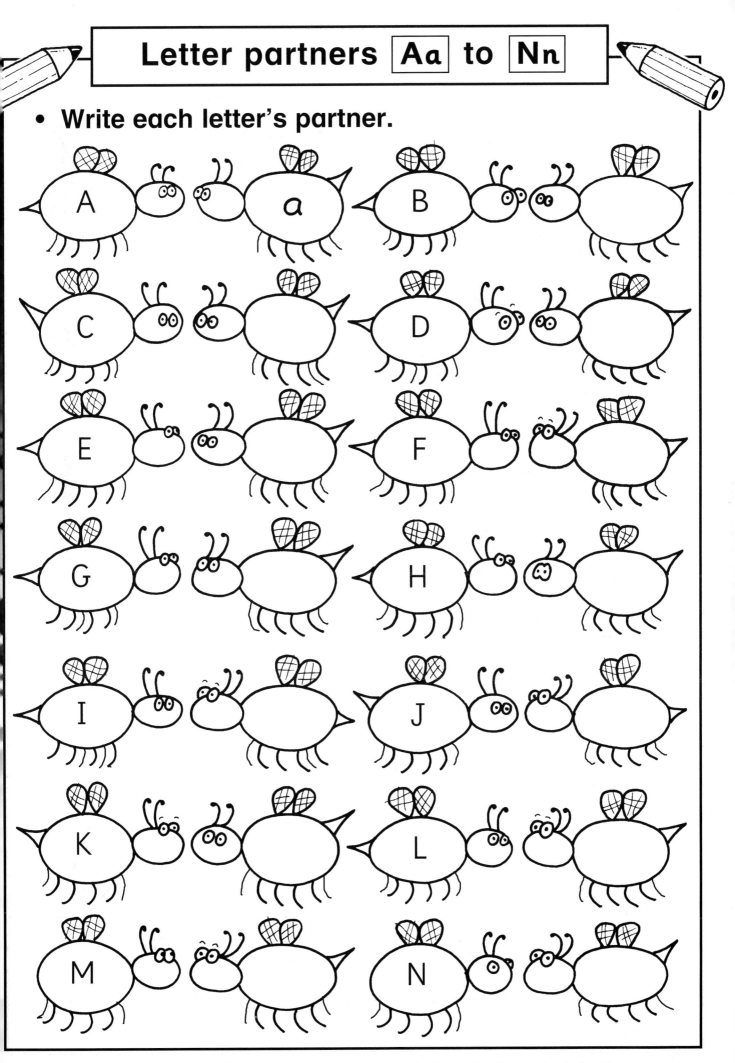

Teachers' note   As an extension, ask the children to write the names of three people which begin with letters from **A** to **N**. Ask them to write three words which are not names and which begin with the same letters.

Developing Literacy
Word Level Year R
© A & C Black 1998

21

Letter partners Oo to Zz

- **Write each letter's partner.**

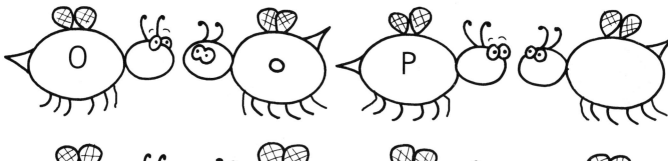

Teachers' note As an extension, ask the children to write the names of three people which begin with letters from **O** to **Z** . Ask them to write three words which are not names and which begin with the same letters.

Developing Literacy
Word Level Year R
© A & C Black 1998

22

• **Match the people to their shopping.**

I am Carly.
I buy things
beginning
with ☐C .

I am Bipin.
I buy things
beginning
with ☐ .

I am Sarah.
I buy things
beginning
with ☐ .

Now try this!

• **Write your name.**

• **Draw your shopping.**

• **Ask a partner to say what you have bought.**

Teachers' note As an extension, this could be continued as a group activity, using different names, and with the children thinking of items which the named people might buy; for example, 'I am David. I bought a doughnut, a duster, a dishcloth and a drink.'

Developing Literacy
Word Level Year R
© A & C Black 1998

People and places

- **The children are in places which begin with the same letter as their names.**
- **Draw lines to join them to the places.**

Bill

Paul

Tania

Harriet

Cara

Raju

Now try this!

- **Draw three other people in places which begin with the same letter as their names.**

Teachers' note After the activity the children could play a group or class game in which they have to suggest hiding-places for children which begin with the same letters as their names; for example, 'Danny hid behind the door'.

Developing Literacy
Word Level Year R
© A & C Black 1998

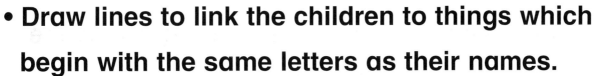

Name link

- **Draw lines to link the children to things which begin with the same letters as their names.**
- **Use a different colour for each child.**

- **Write your name.**

- **Cut out or draw pictures of things that begin with the same letter as your name.**

Teachers' note Encourage the children to say the names of the objects depicted.

Developing Literacy
Word Level Year R
© A & C Black 1998

25

- **Read the words.**

| I | me | he | she |

- **Colour** | I | - red | me | - blue

  | he | - green | she | - yellow

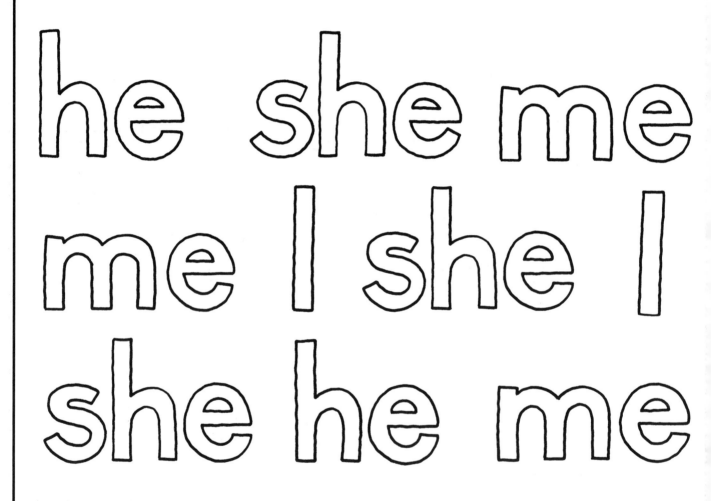

he she me

me I she I

she he me

Now try this!

- **Copy the words.**

I   me   he   she

Teachers' note Introduce the words by writing them on a blackboard and then asking the children to write them 'in the air' with their fingers. After the activity, ask the children to Look, Say, Cover, Write and Check the words. Remind them that **I** always has a capital letter.

Developing Literacy
Word Level Year R
© A & C Black 1998

- **Read the words.**

| said | you | they | we |

- **Colour** | said | - red | you | - blue

| they | - green | we | - yellow

Now try this!

- **Copy the words.**

said   you   they   we

_____

Teachers' note Introduce the words by writing them on a blackboard and then asking the children to write them in the air with their fingers. After the activity, ask them to Look, Say, Cover, Write and Check the words.

Developing Literacy
Word Level Year R
© A & C Black 1998

Word work 3

- **Read the words on the tree trunk.**

- **Copy them under their rhyming**

  words on the leaves.

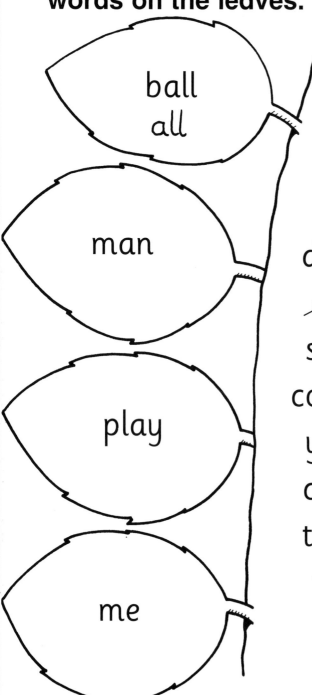

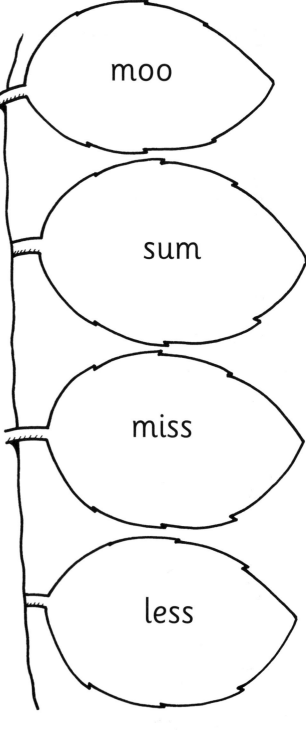

ball
all

moo

man

sum

day
all
see
come
yes
can
this
to

play

miss

me

less

Now
try
this!

- **Write another rhyming word on each leaf.**

Teachers' note Remind the children that the rhyming words will not necessarily be spelled the same, for example, **me** and **see**.

Developing Literacy
Word Level Year R
© A & C Black 1998

Word work 4

• **Read the words.**

| on | at | in | am | it |

• **Complete the sentences with these words.**

| on | at | in | am | it |

	The wig is ____ the pig.
	What time is ____?
	I ____ five.
	The doll is ____ the box.
	We are ____ school.

Teachers' note First, give each child a card bearing one of the words. Say each word in turn: the children put up their hands when they hear their word. Let them exchange cards and then repeat this. After the activity, ask the children to Look, Say, Cover, Write and Check the words.

Developing Literacy
Word Level Year R
© A & C Black 1998

29

• **Read the words in the shapes.**

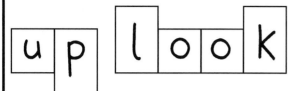  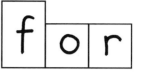

• **Copy the words into the shapes.**

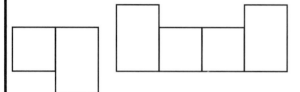 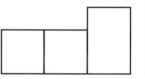 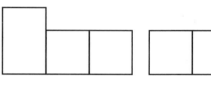

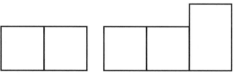 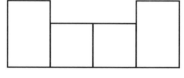 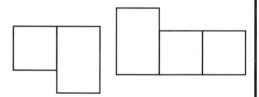

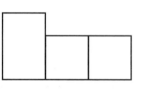 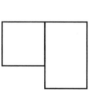 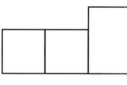 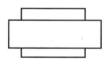 

Now try this!

• **Look**	• **Say**	• **Cover**	• **Write**	• **Check**
up			up	✓ ✗
look			_____	
and			_____	
for			_____	
no			_____	

Teachers' note Introduce this by drawing the shapes of the words on the activity sheet on to a large piece of squared paper (using 1cm squares). Write each word into its shape. Repeat this, asking the children to point out the shape of each word.

Developing Literacy
Word Level Year R
© A & C Black 1998

Word work 6

• **Read the words in the shapes.**

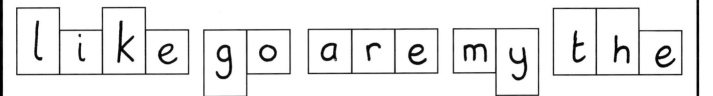

l i k e g o a r e m y t h e

• **Copy the words into the shapes.**

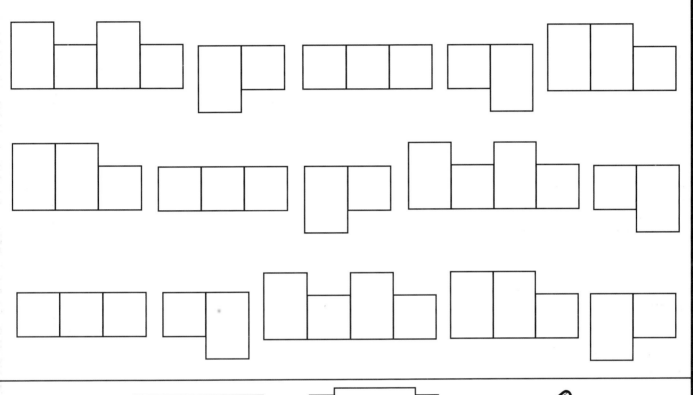

like [ ] like ✓ ✗

• **Look**   • **Say**   • **Cover**   • **Write**   • **Check**

Now try this!

like _____

go _____

are _____

my _____

the _____

Teachers' note After the children have completed this they could copy a word, in colour, into 1cm squares marked on a large piece of squared paper. Display their words.

Developing Literacy
Word Level Year R
© A & C Black 1998

Kitchen things

• **Match the labels to the kitchen things.**

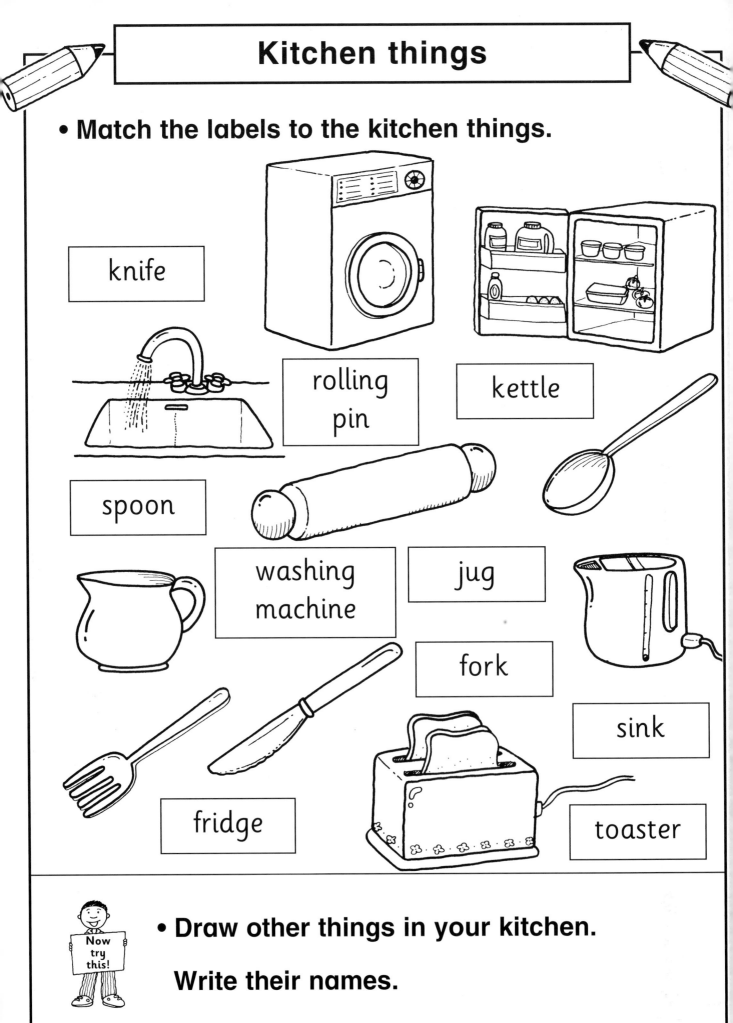

knife

rolling pin

kettle

spoon

washing machine

jug

fork

sink

fridge

toaster

• **Draw other things in your kitchen.**

Write their names.

Now try this!

Teachers' note   During the whole class introduction, show the children pictures of kitchens and ask them to name the things they see in them. Provide labels which they can match to the objects.

Developing Literacy
Word Level Year R
© A & C Black 1998

Classroom things

- **Label the classroom things.**

- **Use a picture dictionary to help you.**

b _ook_ _____

ch _____

t _____

p _____

f _____ t _____

d _____

p _____

b _____

g _____

b _____

t _____

- **Draw three other things in your classroom.**

- **Write their names.**

Now try this!

Developing Literacy
Word Level Year R
© A & C Black 1998

Teachers' note Label the objects in the classroom which are shown on the activity sheet, and others which the children might find useful. Attach the labels so that they can be easily removed; after the children have completed the sheet, ask them to fix the labels back on to the objects.

- **Cut out the pictures.**

- **Say each word.**

- **Does it begin with the same letter as** ball **or** doll **?**

- **Glue it on to the chart.**

b	d

Now try this!

- **Draw three other things which begin with the same letter as** ball **or** doll **.**

Teachers' note The children could first cut out and collect pictures, from catalogues, magazines or old colouring books, of things which begin with **b** and **d**. Ask them to sort them into two sets (beginning with the same letter as ball or doll).

Developing Literacy
Word Level Year R
© A & C Black 1998

- **Cut out the pictures.**

- **Say each word.**

- **Does it begin with the same letter as** mat **or** net **?**

- **Glue it on to the chart.**

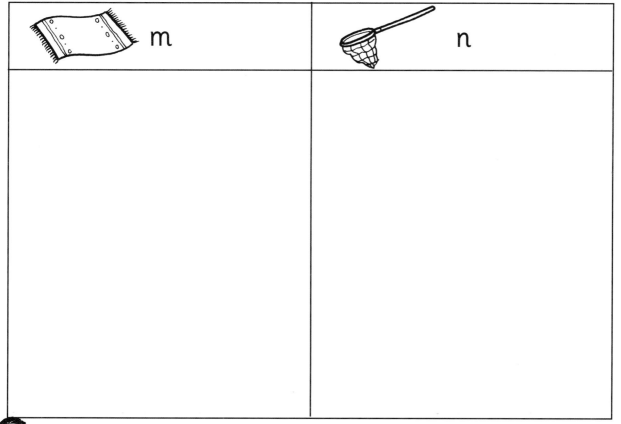

m

n

- **Draw other things which begin with the same letter as** mat **or** net **.**

Teachers' note After this activity, the children could make an **m** booklet and an **n** booklet into which they glue pictures of things which begin with that letter.

Developing Literacy
Word Level Year R
© A & C Black 1998

First sounds bingo cards

Teachers' note Glue or photocopy pages 36 and 37 on to card. Cut each into two bingo cards. Cut out the letters on page 38. Give each child a bingo card and scrap paper with which to cover pictures which are 'called'. Show a letter card. What sound is it? The children cover any pictures which begin with it.

**Developing Literacy
Word Level Year R**
© A & C Black 1998

First sounds bingo cards

Teachers' note Pages 36 and 37 together provide four bingo cards for **First sounds bingo** (see the notes for page 36).

Developing Literacy
Word Level Year R
© A & C Black 1998

37

First sounds letter cards

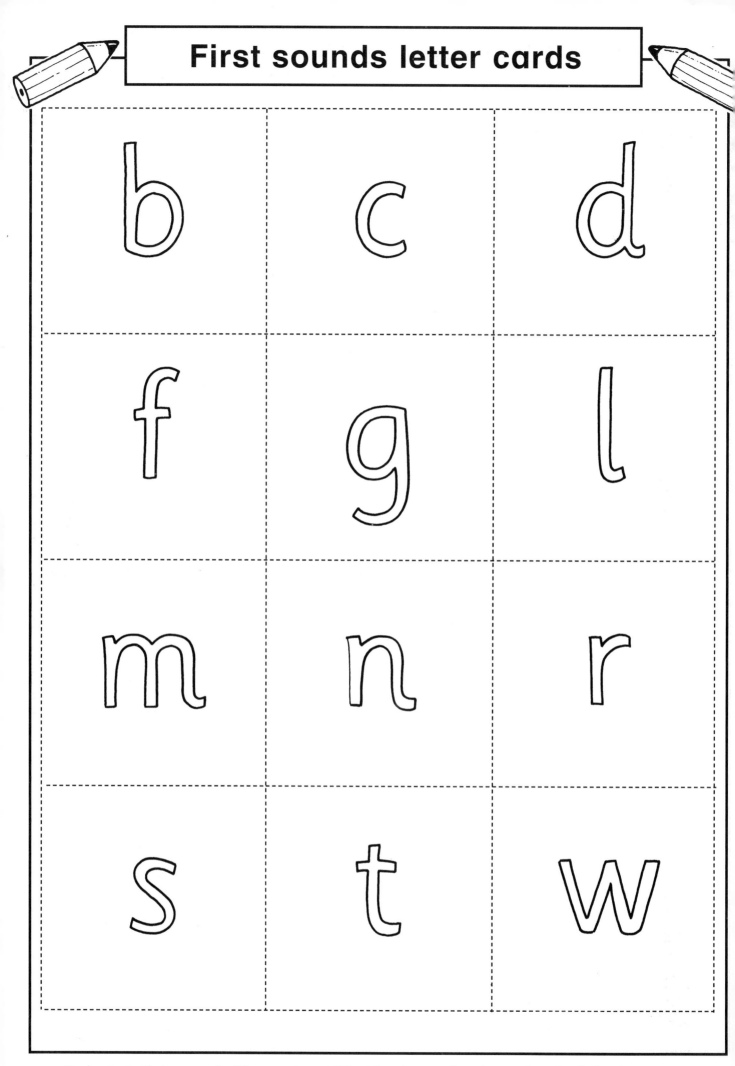

b   c   d

f   g   l

m   n   r

s   t   w

Teachers' note Photocopy or glue this page onto card. Cut out these letters and use them to play 'First sounds bingo' with the bingo cards from pages 36 and 37.

Developing Literacy
Word Level Year R
© A & C Black 1998

First sounds $\boxed{b}$, $\boxed{m}$, $\boxed{c}$

- **Write the missing letters.**
- **Say the words.**

<u>b</u> at

_ op

_ ot

_ ar

_ ed

_ at

_ ug

_ up

_ in

 **• Cut out and collect pictures to make a $\boxed{b}$ page, an $\boxed{m}$ page and a $\boxed{c}$ page.**

Now try this!

Teachers' note Encourage the children to say the names of the objects in the pictures before and after they have completed the words. The children's pages could be made into a **b** book, an **m** book and a **c** book.

Developing Literacy
Word Level Year R
© A & C Black 1998

- **Write the missing letters.**
- **Say the words.**

  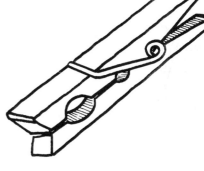

_ at   _ aw   _ eg

_ ad   _ ut   _ an

_ en   _ un   _ en

 • **Cut out and collect pictures to make an h page, a p page and an s page.**

Teachers' note Encourage the children to say the names of the objects in the pictures before and after they have completed the words. The children's pages could be made into an **h** book, a **p** book and an **s** book.

Developing Literacy
Word Level Year R
© A & C Black 1998

Starting with sh

- **Colour the things which start with** sh.

- **In the boxes, draw three other things which start with** sh.

Now try this!

Teachers' note Ask the children to find pictures of, and to think of, things at home or at school which begin with **sh**. They could take turns to contribute to a story which begins 'Shazia had a shower. Shazia put on her shoes ...' and so on.

Developing Literacy
Word Level Year R
© A & C Black 1998

41

- **Make words which start with** sh.
- **Read the words.**

__ __ ip

__ __ ell

__ __ eep

__ __ ed

__ __ op

__ __ oe

Now try this!

- **Write other words which start with** sh.
- **Read the words.**

Teachers' note Once the children can recognise the **sh** sound in speech they can practise writing it. This activity could be introduced or reinforced by teaching the children the tongue-twister 'She sells sea shells on the sea shore', ask the children to write the complete words.

**Developing Literacy
Word Level Year R
© A & C Black 1998**

Starting with **ch**

• Colour the things which start with **ch** .

• With a partner, name three other things which start with **ch** .

Teachers' note The children could contribute to a **ch** display which might contain pictures of chips, chimpanzees and other things which begin with **ch**, as well as pictures with words for actions, such as 'The car chugged up the hill', 'Charles chased the chicken' and so on.

Developing Literacy
Word Level Year R
© A & C Black 1998

43

- **Make words which start with ch.**
- **Read the words.**

___ ___ ips

___ ___ eese

___ ___ ess

___ ___ ocolate

___ ___ erry

___ ___ ick

- **Write three other words which start with ch.**
- **Read the words.**

Teachers' note Introduce this by playing a guessing game with the children: give them definitions and ask them to supply the **ch** word, for example, 'I eat them with salt and vinegar', 'This is a small red fruit'. The children could also write the complete words.

Developing Literacy
Word Level Year R
© A & C Black 1998

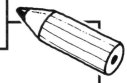

• **Colour the things which start with** th.

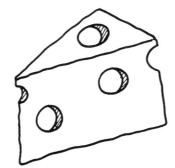
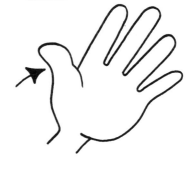

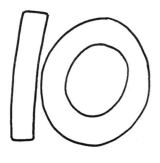

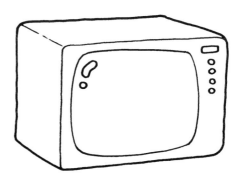

• **Say three other words which begin with** th.

• **Write them.**

Teachers' note Help the children to check the spellings of the words they have written. Read aloud a story which has several words which begin with the sound **th**. Ask the children to put up their hands when they hear a word which begins with **th**; what was the word?

Developing Literacy
Word Level Year R
© A & C Black 1998

45

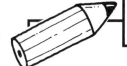

- **Complete the** th **words under the pictures.**
- **Say the words.**

thumb	thrush	three
third	thistle	thirty

_ _ umb	_ _ rush	_ _ ree
_ _ ird	_ _ istle	_ _ irty

Now try this!

- **Write four other words which start with** th **.**

Teachers' note Help the children to check the spellings of the words they have written. Ask them to write the complete words. After this activity the children could begin a word bank of **th** words, including the, this, that, then, they and them.

46

Developing Literacy
Word Level Year R
© A & C Black 1998

End sounds

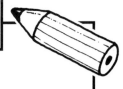

- **Say the words.**

- **Join the things with the same end sound.**

- **Draw three things with the same end sounds as these.**

Teachers' note Introduce the activity by asking the children to listen to a list of words, for example, rib, sob, cab, dab, rub, cub, cob. What do they notice? Begin saying another set of words, and ask the children to continue it, for example; had, led, rid.....

Developing Literacy
Word Level Year R
© A & C Black 1998

47

Word trees

- **Say the word on each leaf.**
- **Listen to its end sound.**
- **Write it on the tree trunk.**

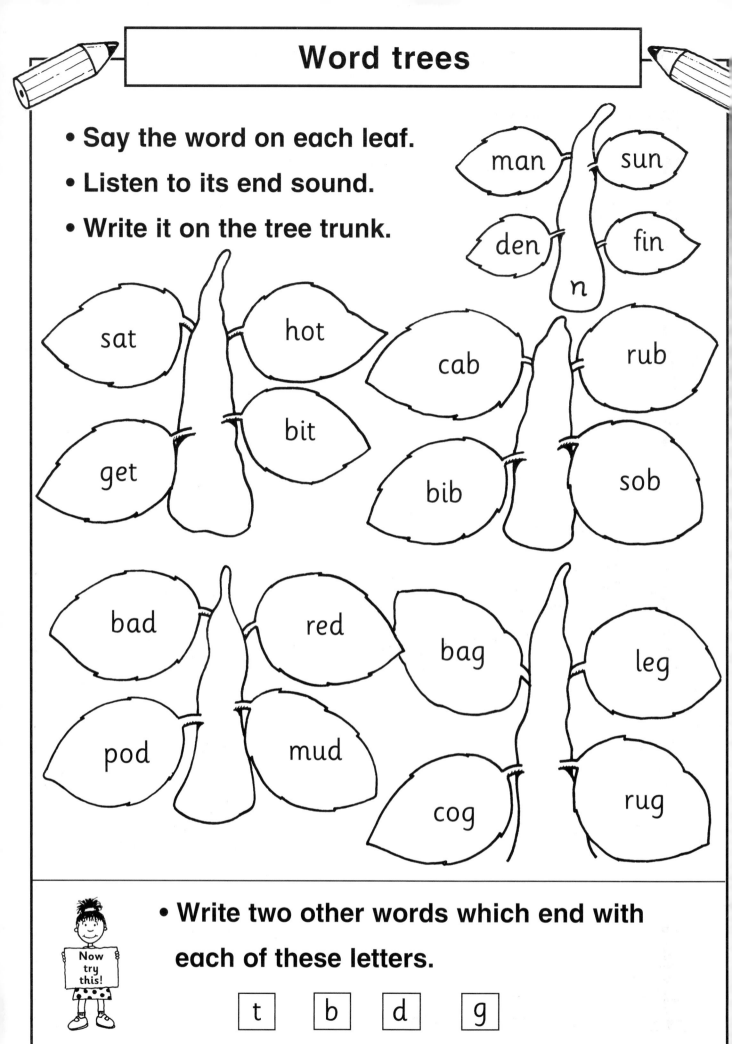

man   sun   den   fin   n

sat   hot   cab   rub   bit   get   bib   sob

bad   red   bag   leg   pod   mud   cog   rug

- **Write two other words which end with each of these letters.**

| t | b | d | g |

Teachers' note Encourage the children to listen to the final sounds of words. Say some consonant-vowel-consonant words and ask them to write the final sounds, for example, pot, fat, sit, pet, dab, rob, cob, tab, bed, sad, hid, cod, rag, beg, big, tug.

Developing Literacy
Word Level Year R
© A & C Black 1998

- **Finish the words.**

- **Write the words on the spaceships.**

- **Say the words.**

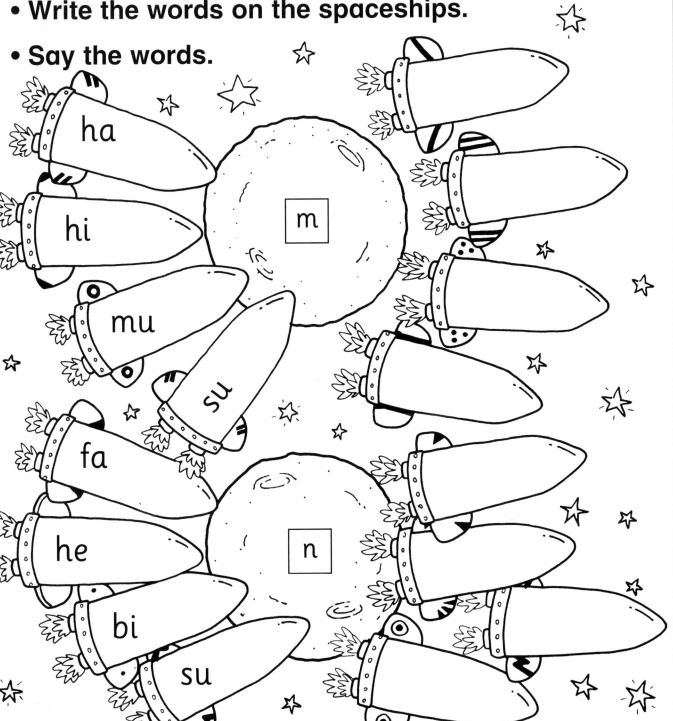

- **Write four other words which end**

  with m and n.

- **Say the words.**

Teachers' note When they have completed this activity the children can read to a partner the words they have made. If any of their answers differ, they can check which is correct.

Developing Literacy
Word Level Year R
© A & C Black 1998

Endings p and y

- **Finish the words.**
- **Write the words on the spaceships.**
- **Say the words.**

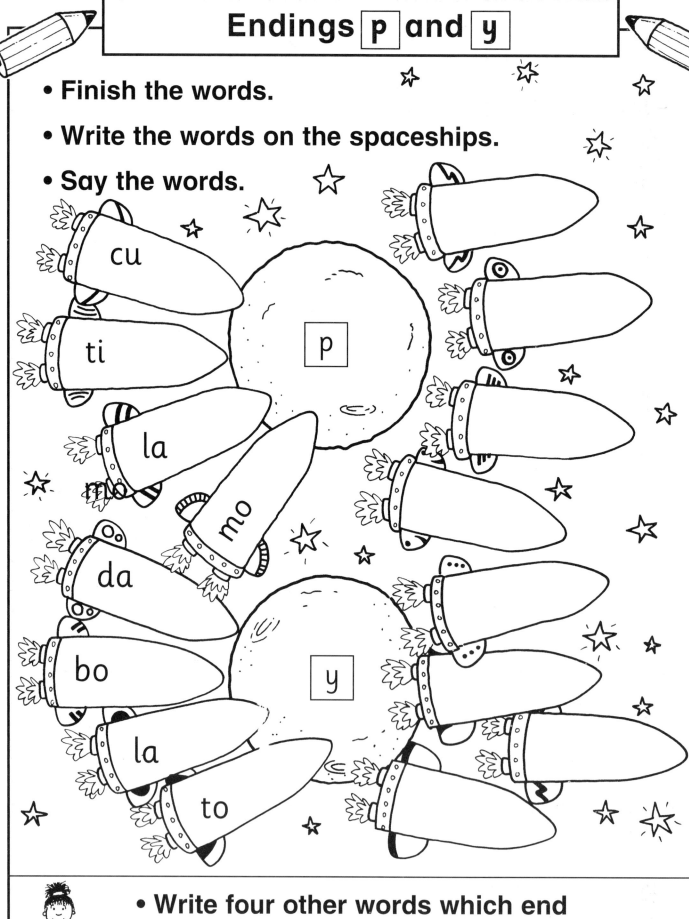

cu

ti

la

mo

p

da

bo

la

to

y

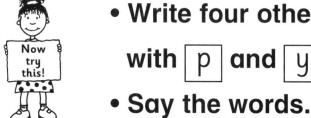

Now
try
this!

- **Write four other words which end**

  with p and y.
- **Say the words.**

Teachers' note When they have completed this activity the children can read to a partner the words they have made. If any of their answers differ, they can check which is correct.

Developing Literacy
Word Level Year R
© A & C Black 1998

• **Join the things which rhyme.**

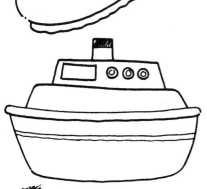

• **Draw two things which rhyme with each**

of these.

Teachers' note Introduce the idea of rhyme by encouraging the children to join in repeated rhymes in stories, for example, the chorus from *The Gingerbread Man.*

Developing Literacy
Word Level Year R
© A & C Black 1998

Rhyme line

• **Colour the thing which does not rhyme.**

 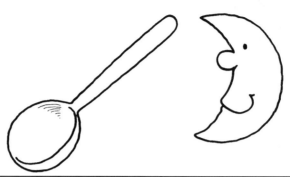 

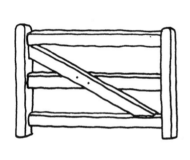   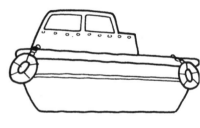

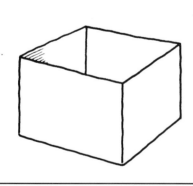   

 • **Draw two things which rhyme with each**

of these.

Teachers' note Introduce the activity by reading aloud lists of four words in which all but one rhyme, for example: beak, soak, seek, leak; road, bead, toad, load; send, bend, mend, meat. Ask the children which word does not rhyme.

Developing Literacy
Word Level Year R
© A & C Black 1998

Rhyming pairs

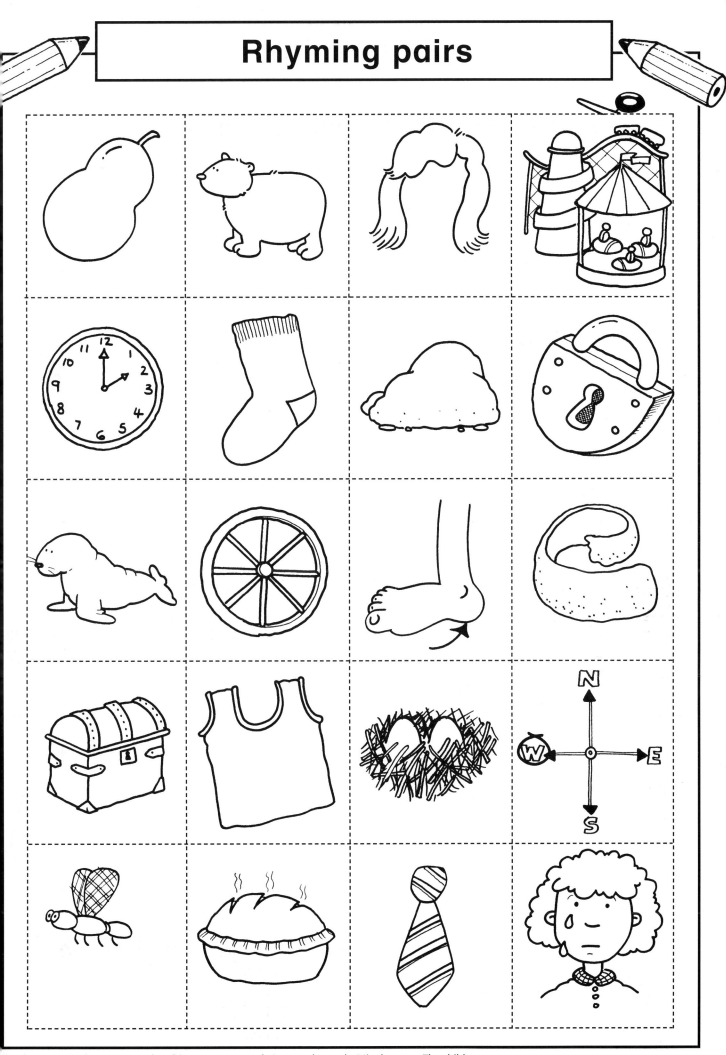

Teachers' note Photocopy or glue this page on to card. Cut out the cards. Mix them up. The children sort them into sets of rhyming words. To play 'Rhyming pairs', shuffle the cards and place them face down. The children turn over two cards: if they rhyme, they keep them, if not, they turn them back.

Developing Literacy
Word Level Year R
© A & C Black 1998

53

Rhyme writing

- Say the word for each picture.

- Write the word.

- Write words which rhyme with it.

n <u>e</u> t

b <u>e</u> t
l _ _
v _ _
w _ _

b _ _
d _ _
f _ _
t _ _
w _ _

b _ _
r _ _
s _ _
t _ _
w _ _

c _ _
p _ _
s _ _
_ _

Now try this!

- Write two words which rhyme with each of these.

Teachers' note The children could make up silly sentences, using the rhyming words, to share with the rest of the class, for example, 'The tin bin made a din'. Write and display their sentences.

Developing Literacy
Word Level Year R
© A & C Black 1998

The words in each set have the same ending.

- **Write the ending.**

- **Write the word.**

- **Say the word.**

j + | am | = jam

d + [ ] = _____

h + [ ] = _____

P + [ ] = _____

T + | im | = Tim

d + | im | = _dim_

h + [ ] = _____

K + [ ] = _____

b + | un | = bun

f + [ ] = _____

g + [ ] = _____

r + [ ] = _____

h + | ut | = hut

b + [ ] = _____

c + [ ] = _____

n + [ ] = _____

Now try this!

- **Write another word which ends with each of these.**

| am | | im | | un | | ut |

Teachers' note Introduce the activity by showing the children flash cards on to which the words in the activity have been copied. Ask them to sort them into groups with the same rime. Different ideas have been given for using **Beginnings and endings 1-3** on pages 56 and 57.

Developing Literacy
Word Level Year R
© A & C Black 1998

The words in each set have the same ending.

- **Write the ending.**
- **Write the word.**
- **Say the word.**

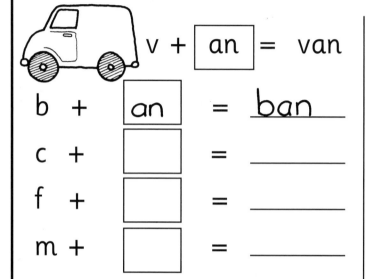

v + | an | = van

b + | an | = _ban_

c + | | = _____

f + | | = _____

m + | | = _____

h + | en | = hen

B + | | = _____

d + | | = _____

L + | | = _____

m + | | = _____

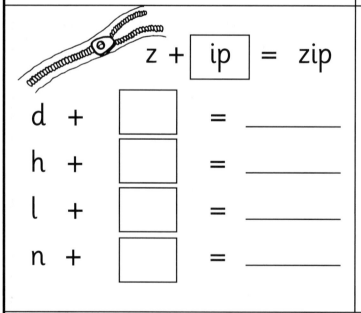

z + | ip | = zip

d + | | = _____

h + | | = _____

l + | | = _____

n + | | = _____

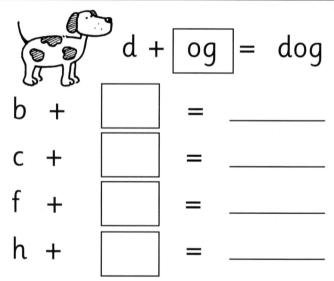

d + | og | = dog

b + | | = _____

c + | | = _____

f + | | = _____

h + | | = _____

Now try this!

- **Write another word which ends with each of these.**

| an | | en | | ip | | og |

Teachers' note After the children have completed the activity, encourage them to make up simple sentences with the words they have made, for example: 'Pam eats jam', 'Put the nut in the hut'. Write and display their sentences, for which they could paint pictures.

Developing Literacy
Word Level Year R
© A & C Black 1998

Beginnings and endings 3

The words in each set have the same ending.

- **Write the ending.**

- **Write the word.**

- **Say the word.**

  c + $\boxed{at}$ = cat

b + $\boxed{at}$ = _bat_

f + $\boxed{}$ = _____

m + $\boxed{}$ = _____

p + $\boxed{}$ = _____

s + $\boxed{}$ = _____

 p + $\boxed{ig}$ = pig

d + $\boxed{}$ = _____

f + $\boxed{}$ = _____

j + $\boxed{}$ = _____

r + $\boxed{}$ = _____

w + $\boxed{}$ = _____

 c + $\boxed{ot}$ = cot

d + $\boxed{}$ = _____

g + $\boxed{}$ = _____

j + $\boxed{}$ = _____

l + $\boxed{}$ = _____

n + $\boxed{}$ = _____

  m + $\boxed{ug}$ = mug

b + $\boxed{}$ = _____

d + $\boxed{}$ = _____

h + $\boxed{}$ = _____

r + $\boxed{}$ = _____

t + $\boxed{}$ = _____

Now try this!

- **Write another word which ends with each of these.**

$\boxed{at}$ $\boxed{ig}$ $\boxed{ot}$ $\boxed{ug}$

Teachers' note From this page (and pages 55 and 56 if desired) copy the words onto cards and pin a card on to the front of each child's clothing (or ask them to hold it). Ask the children to find others whose words rhyme with theirs.

Developing Literacy
Word Level Year R
© A & C Black 1998

Odd one out

- **What is in each picture? Say the words.**

- **Listen to the middle sounds.**

- **Colour the odd one out.**

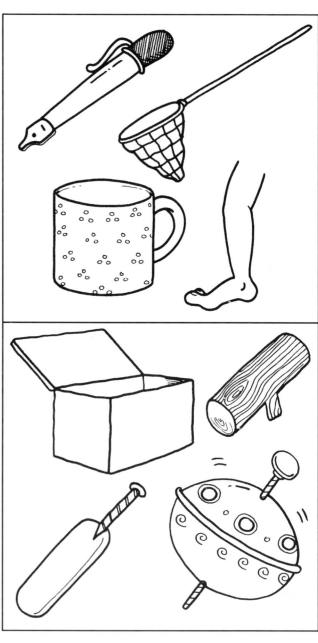

- **Draw things which have the same middle sound as**

Teachers' note   Introduce this by saying 'consonant-vowel-consonant' words which have the same middle sounds, for example: sat, fan, can, rag, tab. What do the children notice? Repeat this activity, adding an 'odd one out'; ask the children to put up their hands when they hear the odd one out.

Developing Literacy
Word Level Year R
© A & C Black 1998

Middle sounds pairs

Teachers' note Photocopy or glue the page on to card. Cut out the pictures. Ask the children to say the names of the objects. To help them to identify the middle sounds, they could choose a picture, say what it is and then find another with the same middle vowel sound.

Developing Literacy
Word Level Year R
© A & C Black 1998

- **Write the middle sounds.**

  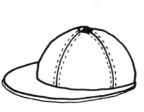

r _ t   b _ g   c _ p

p _ g   s _ x   p _ n

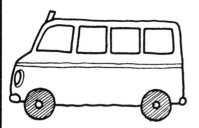  

b _ s   b _ n   b _ d

c _ t   b _ x   d _ g

- **Draw another picture for each line.**
- **Write the word.**

Teachers' note The children should look at the pictures and say the words before writing the missing middle letters. Encourage them to say other words with the same middle vowel sounds. Challenge the more able children to write the longest lists they can of words with each middle sound.

Developing Literacy
Word Level Year R
© A & C Black 1998

Naughty Teddy

- **Naughty Teddy is hiding the middle letter.**
- **What might the word be?**
- **Say it.**
- **Write the letter.**
- **Write the word.**

b ☐ t

a

bat

Teachers' note   Encourage the children to read each word by guessing a vowel which will fit. The children might read different words, for example, s-t could be 'sat', 'set' or 'sit'. Any of these is correct.

Developing Literacy
Word Level Year R
© A & C Black 1998

61

Partners

- Say the words.
- Join the pairs which have the same middle sound.

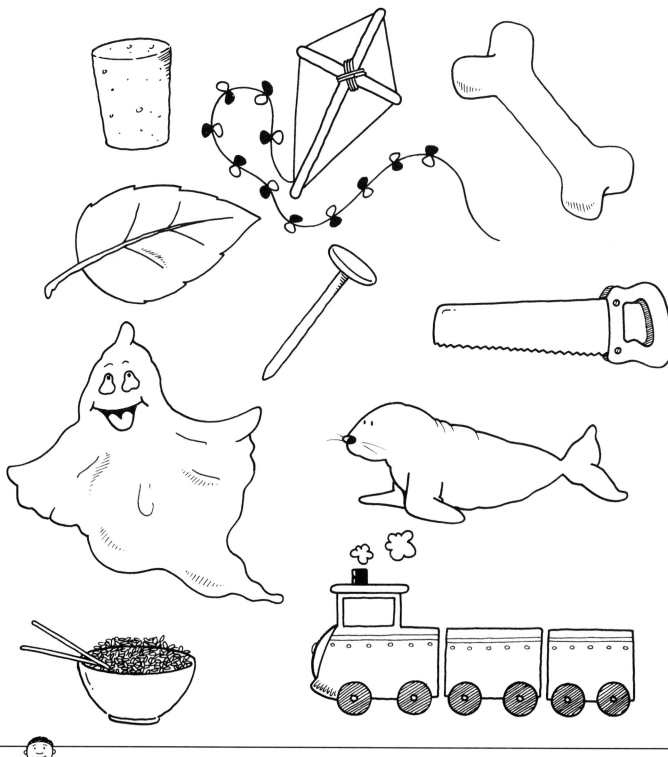

 • Make up other word partners.

Teachers' note Say a word whose dominant phoneme is easy to recognise, such as 'brown'. Write it and ask the children to repeat it. What is the main sound they notice (**ow**)? Tell them to listen to the words you say and to put up their hands when they hear a word with the same main sound as 'brown'.

Developing Literacy
Word Level Year R
© A & C Black 1998

Teachers' note Photocopy or glue this and page 64 on to card. These are a flexible resource which could be used in a variety of ways. Mix them up and ask the children to sort them into sets of words with the same dominant phoneme (main sound). The instructions for 'Happy sound families' are on page 64. The picture cards could also be used to play 'Pairs' or 'Snap'.

Developing Literacy
Word Level Year R
© A & C Black 1998

Happy sound families 2

Teachers' note   Give each child a card from a different 'family' of middle sounds, for example: rope, soap, boat, rose. Shuffle the cards and place them face down. The children turn over a card and keep any which match their 'family': they turn back any which do not. Once they have completed their family of four, they can start collecting another family.

Developing Literacy
Word Level Year R
© A & C Black 1998